Songs of Inspiration

Artistic Piano Arrangements of New Latter-day Saint Hymns

Lynn S. Lund

ISBN: 0-88290-276-8
Horizon Publishers Catalog & Order No.: 2903

Printed and distributed
in the United States of America by

Horizon
Publishers
& Distributors, Incorporated

50 South 500 West P.O. Box 490
Bountiful, Utah 84010-0490

Contents

Each Life That Touches Ours For Good

Karen Lynn Davidson

A. Laurence Lyon
Arr. by Lynn S. Lund

This arrangement Copyright© 1986
by Horizon Publishers & Distributors, Inc.

8

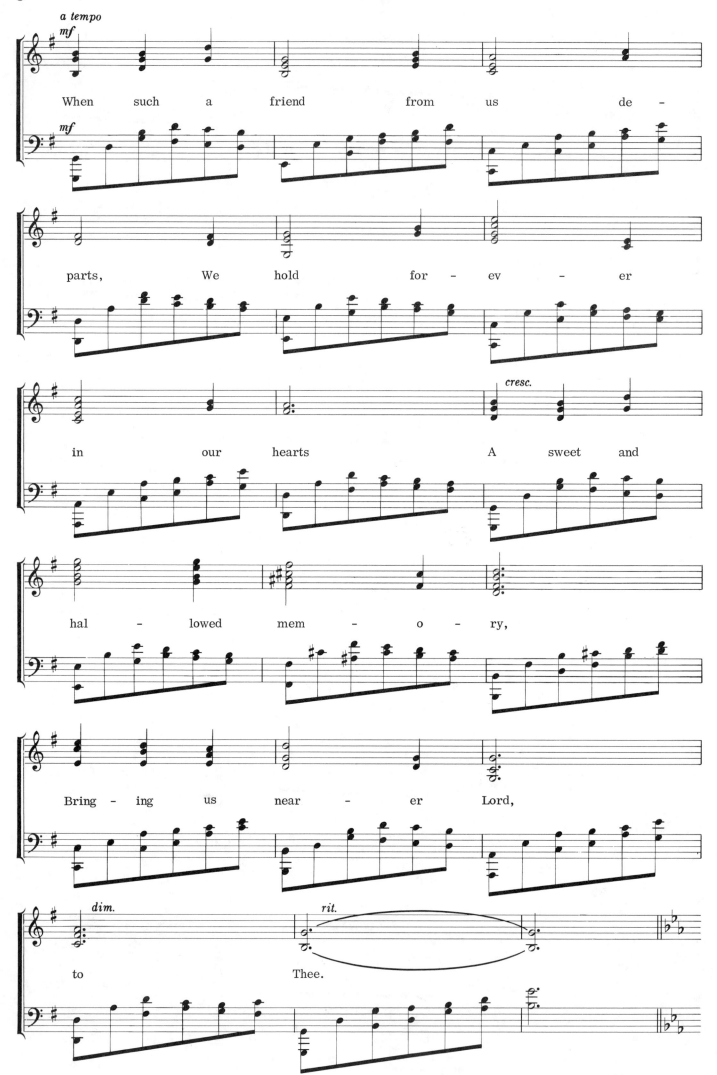

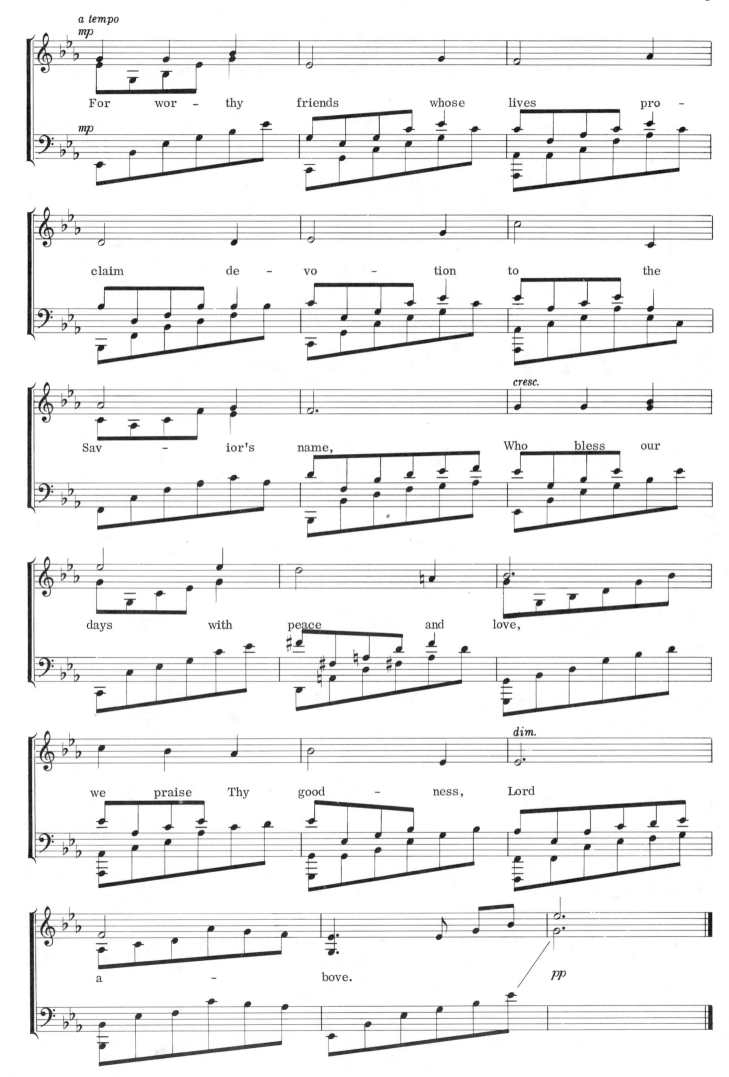

Teach Me to Walk in the Light

Clara W. McMaster

Clara W. McMaster
Arr. by Lynn S. Lund

This arrangement Copyright© 1986
by Horizon Publishers & Distributors, Inc.

Our Savior's Love

Edward L. Hart

Crawford Gates
Arr. by Lynn S. Lund

This arrangement Copyright© 1986
by Horizon Publishers & Distributors, Inc.

Lord, I Would Follow Thee

Susan Evans McCloud

Newell Dayley
Arr. by Lynn S. Lund

This arrangement Copyright© 1986
by Horizon Publishers & Distributors, Inc.

Families Can Be Together Forever

Ruth M. Gardner

Vanja Y. Watkins
Arr. by Lynn S. Lund

This arrangement Copyright© 1986
by Horizon Publishers & Distributors, Inc.

As I Search the Holy Scriptures

C. Marianne Johnson Fisher

C. Marianne Johnson Fisher
Arr. by Lynn S. Lund

This arrangement Copyright© 1986
by Horizon Publishers & Distributors, Inc.

As I search the ho - ly script - ures, May Thy mer - cy

be re - vealed. Soothe my trou - bled heart and spir - it;

May my un - seen wounds be healed. As I search the

ho - ly script - ures, Help me pon - der and o - bey.

In Thy word is life e - ter - nal; May Thy light show

me the way.

God's Daily Care

Marie C. Turk

Willy Reske
Arr. by Lynn S. Lund

As I watch the ris - ing sun   When the day has

just be - gun,   I am think - ing   of the love

that comes dai - ly   from a - bove.

This arrangement Copyright© 1986
by Horizon Publishers & Distributors, Inc.

Fa - ther turn Thy ear to me; Let me of - fer thanks to Thee.

For Thy wise and ten - der care. Of Thy chil - dren eve - ry - where.

I Know My Father Lives

Reid N. Nibley

Reid N. Nibley
Arr. by Lynn S. Lund

This arrarngement Copyright© 1986
by Horizon Publishers & Distributors, Inc.

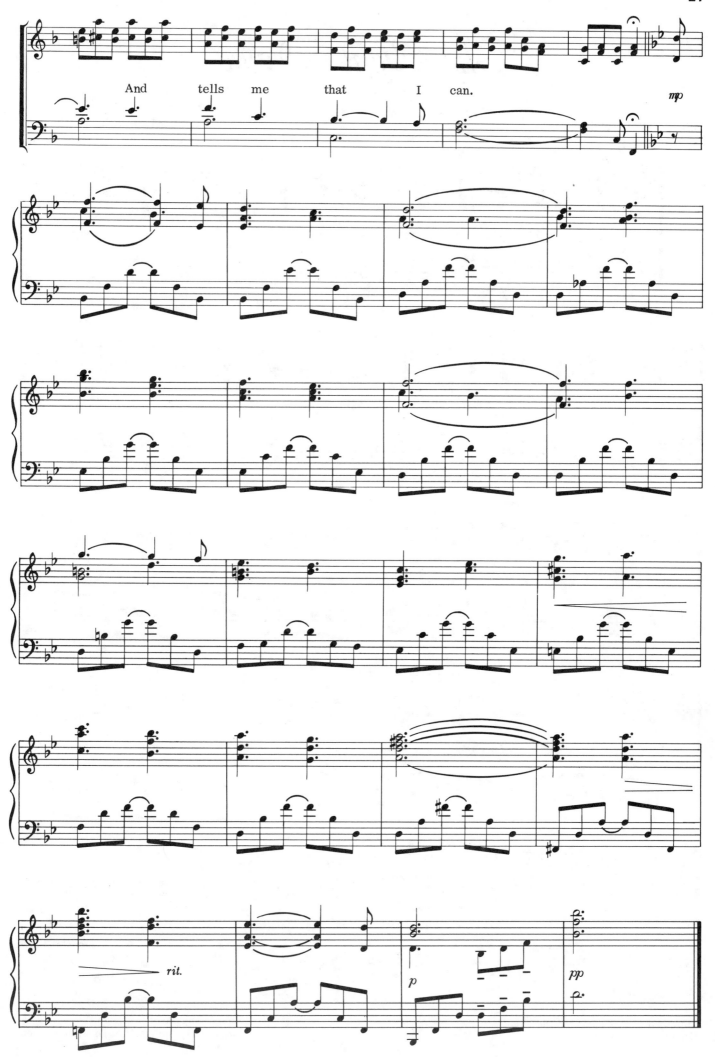

The Light Divine

Matilda Watts Cahoon

Mildred T. Pettit
Arr. by Lynn S. Lund

The light of God rests on the face of brook and flow'r and tree; And kin-dles in our hap-py hearts the hope of things to be. Fa-ther, let thy light di-vine shine on us we pray. Touch our eyes that we may see; Teach us to o-bey. Ours, the sa-cred mis-sion is to bear thy mes-sage

This arrangement Copyright© 1986
by Horizon Publishers & Distributors, Inc.

far. The light of faith is in our hearts,

Truth our guid - ing star. The light of faith a -

bides with - in the heart of ev - 'ry child; Like

buds that wait for blos - som - ing, it grows with ra - diance

mild. Fa - ther, let thy light di - vine

shine on us we pray. Touch our eyes that

30

Help Me Teach With Inspiration

Words and Music Lorin F. Wheelwright

Arr. by Lynn S. Lund

This arrangement used by permission
of the copyright owner, and Copyright©
1986 by Horizon Publishers &
Distributors, Inc.

As Sisters in Zion

Emily H. Woodmansee

Janice Kapp Perry
Arr. by Lynn S. Lund

This arrangement Copyright© 1986
by Horizon Publishers & Distributors, Inc.

give us the wis – dom to tru – ly suc – seed.